D1172191

Written by BENJAMIN ELKIN

SUCH IS THE WAY OF THE WORLD

Illustrated by YOKO MITSUHASHI

PARENTS' MAGAZINE PRESS
NEW YORK

To M.R.

This was an important day.
Desta had a new job. For the very first time
he was in charge of Father's cattle, all by himself.
Now Desta was taking the cattle to the grasslands.
On his shoulder rode his pet monkey, Jima.
Desta patted the cows and hummed a happy tune.
All was right with his world.

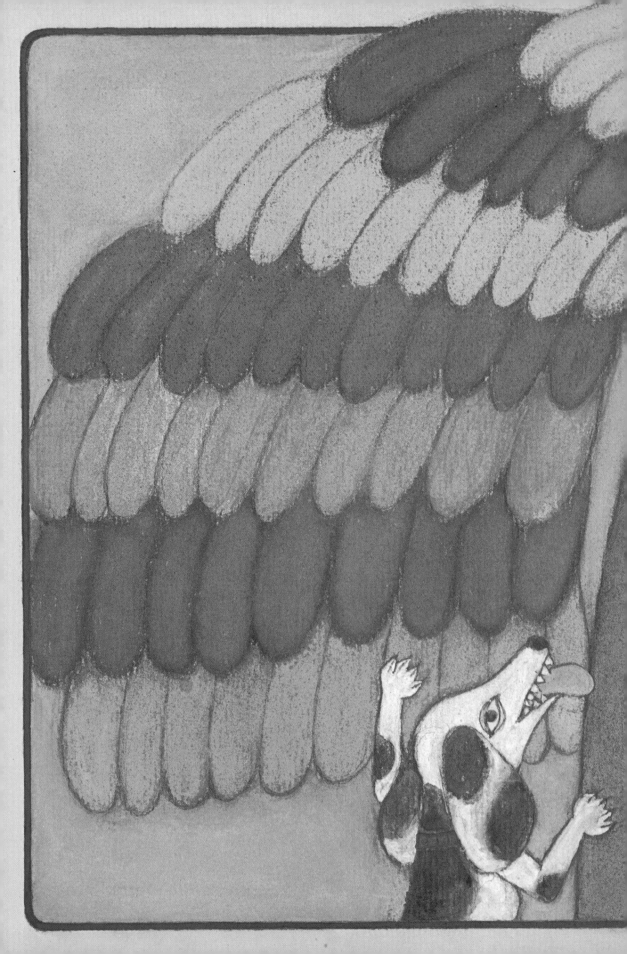

But the world does not stand still.
Suddenly everything changed.
Out of nowhere, a barking dog sprang at Jima.
The frightened monkey leaped for a tree,
and just like that, he was gone.
Only the trembling leaves
showed where he had been.

Desta was only a little boy, so he wailed.
His cries rang through the air. The startled cows
moved faster and soon they were out of sight.
But Desta paid them no mind.

"Hush, lad," said the owner
of the dog. "It is the way of the world that dogs
must hunt and monkeys must flee. Here, you may have
my game board to pay for your lost monkey."
And he tucked the game board under Desta's arm.

The game board was heavy, but Desta hardly noticed it.
Down the road he saw a group of camel drivers around
a fire. So he hurried to ask if they had seen his Jima.

In his haste, Desta bumped
against a saddle on the ground.
The game board flew from
under his arm, right into the flames.

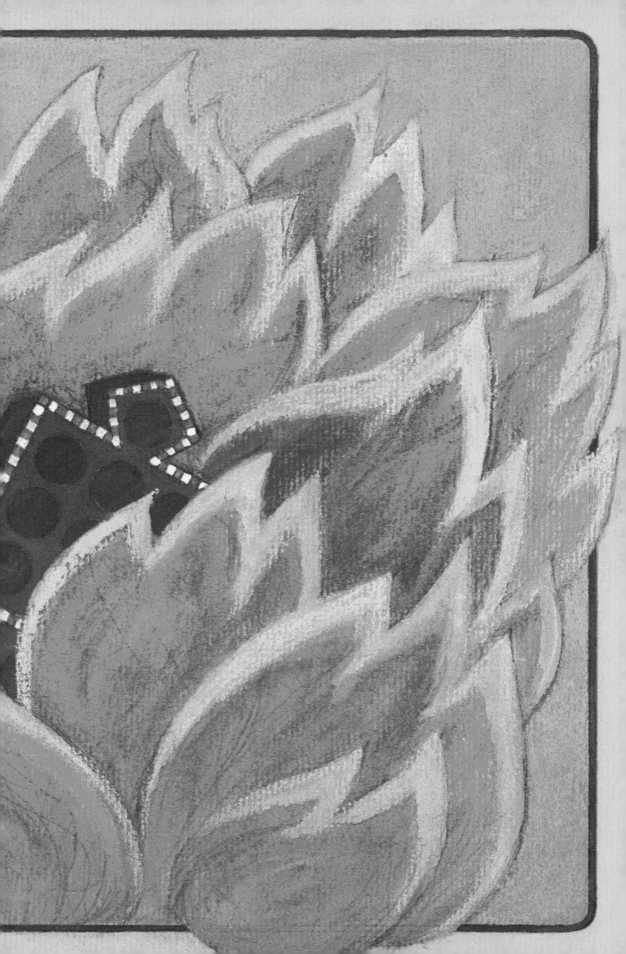

"That was surely my fault,"
said one of the drivers. "I should
not have left the saddle there.
But such is the way of the world.
What is your loss will make our fire that much brighter.
Here, you must have this pot to pay for it."
And he placed a large pot on top of Desta's head.

Desta hardly noticed the pot, either. A quick glance
showed him that no monkey was in sight. By now, Jima
might be in danger somewhere.
He had to find the monkey right away.
From around the bend in the road
came the happy beat of drums.
Maybe Jima was there. Desta ran
and saw villagers getting ready for
a hunting dance. Men in lion skins
and ostrich feathers were holding
spears. But no one was holding
a pet monkey.

A man reached for
the pot on Desta's head.
"I don't have my drum,"
he said. "Let me drum
on that pot of yours."

The drummer struck
only a few beats.
Then CRASH! The pot
was shattered into bits.

"Such is the way of the world," said the man. "I have tried an army of pots, and not one has ever made a good drum. Here, you may have these ostrich feathers to pay for the broken pot."

With the feathers in his hand, Desta hurried on down the road to look for Jima. He was stopped by a woman who was selling things on a straw mat.

"Those feathers are just what I need," she said.
She took the feathers and with a few whisks
she drove away a swarm of buzzing flies.
But just then a gust of wind blew the feathers
out of her hand and far, far away.

"Such is the way of the world," said the woman.
"Things come and things go. Here, take this knife
in exchange. A good knife is a friend for life."

Hastily, Desta accepted the knife. He was anxious to get
on with his search. In the next field Desta saw
a goat herder trying to dig a hole in the hard ground.
"Have you seen a lost
monkey?" asked Desta.

"My boy," said the man, "when you watch goats you see only goats. How about lending me your knife to help with this digging?"

Desta handed over the knife and the goat herder started to dig. But the blade hit a stone and broke.

"I am truly sorry," said the man. "But such is the way of the world. Here, take this coil of rope to pay for the knife. A boy can always find some good use for a rope."

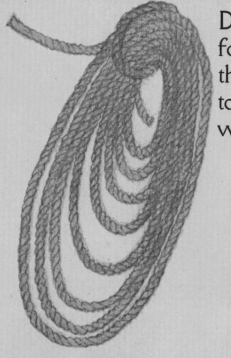

Desta couldn't think of a use for a rope at all. But he put the coil over his arm, then hurried to another field. There, an old man was leaning over a deep well.

Before Desta could ask about Jima,
the man spoke up. "My ox horn canteen
is at the bottom of the well.
Let me use the rope, will you?
Maybe I can fish it out."

The old man made a loop.
He tried to swing
the loop over the ox horn
in the well. But the rope
slipped and fell in, too.

"Such is the way of the world," said the old man. "My troubles always seem to come in pairs. Here, you may have my spear in exchange for your rope."

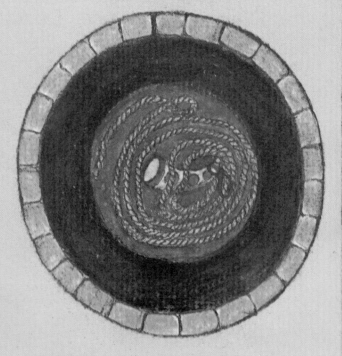

Desta took the spear. Here was something that might help him to rescue Jima. In the distance he saw some hunters. He ran to meet them to ask about his monkey.

But a hunter at once reached out
for the spear. "You must lend us this," he said.
"A lion has been seen near the village
and we need all the weapons we can get."

The man threw the spear at a bush to test its flight.
CRUNCH! The dried-up handle
of the spear spilt in two.

"Such is the way of the world," said the hunter. "It is far better that the spear fail us now rather than when facing a lion. Here, son. In this bag is a little monkey which I just caught. It will make you a nice pet."

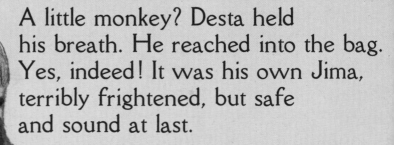

A little monkey? Desta held his breath. He reached into the bag. Yes, indeed! It was his own Jima, terribly frightened, but safe and sound at last.

Desta hugged his pet and started for home. He could think of nothing but the joy of having Jima back again. But then... Ee-yah!

He suddenly remembered Father's cattle.
There they were ahead of him, going home
all by themselves. He ran to catch up with them.

Near the house, Father
and Mother looked up.
They saw Desta bringing
home the cattle.
On his shoulder rode his
pet monkey, Jima.
Desta patted the cows and
hummed a happy tune.
All was right with his world.

Father smiled proudly.
"I am so glad we gave
Desta that little monkey,"
he said. "There is nothing
like a nice pet to keep
a boy's mind on his work.
Such is the way
of the world."

The End